D1154029

SCRIPT   TOM PEYER
PENCILS   JON SOMMARIVA
INKS   KRIS JUSTICE,
SERGE LA POINTE,
PIERRE-ANDRE DERY
COLORS   DAN JACKSON
LETTERS   SNO CONE

COVER   JON SOMMARIVA

READY SET GO!

GoBoy7 ™

ROCKET COMICS ™

PUBLISHER **Mike Richards**
EDITOR **Dave La**
ASSISTANT EDITOR **Katie Mo**
COLLECTION DESIGNER **Darin Fabr**

THIS BOOK COLLECTS ISSUES 1 THROUGH
THE DARK HORSE COMIC-BOOK SERIES GO B

DARK HORSE COMICS,
10956 SE MAIN STR
MILWAUKIE, OR 97

WWW.DARKHORSE.

TO

FIND A COMICS SHOP IN YOUR AREA
THE COMIC SHOP LOCATOR SERVICE TOLL-FREE AT (888) 266-

FIRST EDITION: APRIL 2
ISBN: 1-56971-9.

10 9 8 7 6 5 4 3
PRINTED IN C

WE'RE *THERE*, JONNY. SEE THAT REALLY BIG MOUNTAIN?

WHOA.

THAT'S YOUR UNCLE'S HOUSE.

WHAT DO YOU MEAN?

YOU'LL SEE.

IS HE *REALLY* MY UNCLE?

THEN HOW COME I NEVER SAW HIM?

I GOT THE PAPERS TO PROVE IT.

WELL, JONNY, HE USED TO VISIT ALL THE TIME.

THEN WHEN YOU WERE BORN, HE CAME TO THE HOSPITAL, AND WHEN HE FIRST LAID EYES ON YOUR LITTLE FACE...

...HE RAN OUT PUKING.

WE NEVER SAW HIM AGAIN.

HA HA HA HA

YOU'RE FUNNY.

STRAP IN, CHAMP. I'M TAKING US DOWN --

WHAT'S GOING *ON*? WHERE *AM* I?

WHAT--?

WHERE AM I?

GO-BASE, JONNY. WELCOME.

I'M YOUR UNCLE NOAH.

WHAT'S THE *MATTER* WITH ME? I FEEL SO *WEIRD*--

YOUR SYSTEM HAS BEEN-- WELL, I GUESS YOU'D SAY *AMPED*. I HAD TO PERFORM A--

WHERE'S MY *MOM* AND *DAD*?

WHERE'S MY *MOM* AND *DAD*?

UHHH...

DID THEY TELL YOU *ANYTHING* ABOUT GO-BASE, SON?

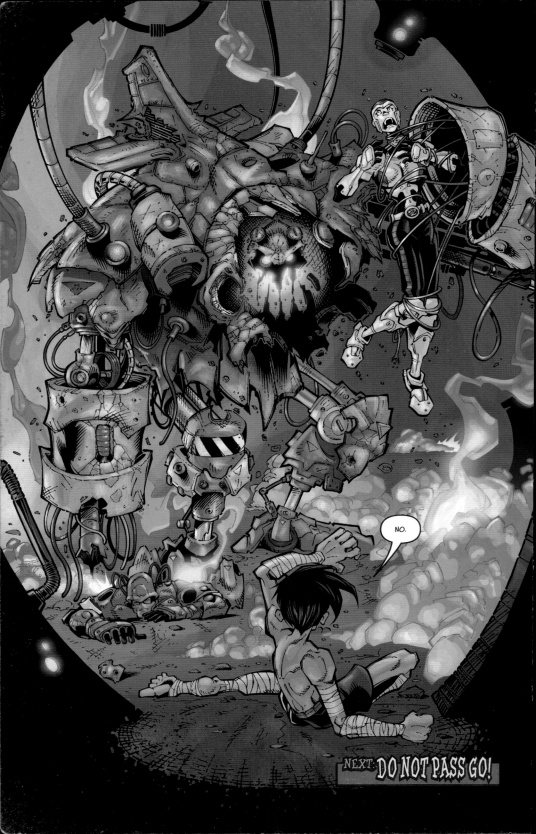

NO...

KANG

YOU KILLED HER! AND...

...AND DAD!

YOU KILLED THEM!

KLAAANG

KLIKLIK

WHAT--?

WAS I OUT?

SKRA

YOUNG MAN.

STOP THIS AT ONCE.

CLAP

CLAP

TO YOUR FEET.

COME ON. I'LL NOT HAVE THIS BEHAVIOR IN MY HOUSE.

WHY?

WHY DOES THAT BOY MAKE ME ASK WHY? I, OF ALL PEOPLE, SHOULDN'T CARE WHY!

AM I NOT THE CULTIST? THE NAPOLEON OF ABSURDITY? DO NOT UNDERLYING REASONS MAKE ME SICK?

WHY ISN'T HE DEAD? HE COULD HAVE DIED IN THE PLANE! HE COULD HAVE BEEN KILLED BY MY SENTIENT KILLING MACHINE!

SIR, I ASSUMED YOU KNEW THAT THE NANOPLASM TRANSFUSION WOULD INCREASE JONNY ZERO'S PHYSICAL CAPACITY--

BUT--

BUT--

OF COURSE I KNEW! THAT IS A REASON! DIDN'T I JUST SAY I HATE REASON?

AREN'T WE LIVING LIKE HERMITS ON THIS FREEZING MOON JUST SO WE CAN DESTROY REASON?

ARE-- ARE YOU GOING TO SCRAP ME, SIR?

IT WOULD MAKE SENSE TO.

LUCKY FOR YOU.

CULTIST? SIR?

THERE IS STILL HOPE. WE CAN STILL ATTACK THEM.

WHOA.

IS THIS WHAT IT'S USUALLY LIKE AROUND HERE? EMERGENCIES AND BAD GUYS AND RISKING YOUR LIFE AND--?

YOU OKAY, KID?

I'M SORRY I PULLED YOU INTO THIS, JONNY.

THE ANSWER IS YES. UNTIL WE FIND A WAY TO DEFEAT THE CULTIST, GO BASE WILL REMAIN ONE OF THE MOST DANGEROUS SPOTS ON EARTH.

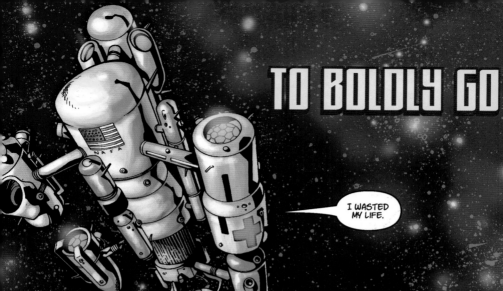

TO BOLDLY GO

I WASTED MY LIFE.

LIKE COMMODORE DECKER IN "THE DOOMSDAY MACHINE?"

NO, RASPLER. LIKE *ME*.

I WASTED MY LIFE EXACTLY LIKE *ME*, NOT LIKE SOME PREPOSTEROUS SCI-FI CHARACTER.

YOU.

I STRUGGLED TO BECOME A PROFESSIONAL PHYSICIST SO I COULD EXCHANGE IDEAS WITH OTHER MINDS OF MY HIGH CALIBER.

THROUGH RIGOROUS STUDY AND SELF-DENIAL I *ATTAINED* MY GOAL, ONLY TO LEARN...

... THAT ALL MY COLLEAGUES EVER WANT TO TALK ABOUT IS *STAR TREK*.

WERE SCIENTISTS SUCH *IDIOTS* BEFORE TELEVISION?

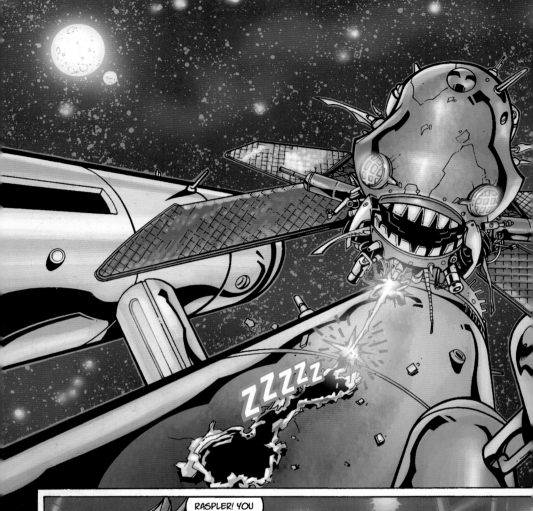

WHAT'S THAT, UNCLE?

BUILDING BLOCKS, JONNY.

OF THE FUTURE.

OF YOU.

YOU MEAN SENT-CHINT NANOPLASM?

EXACTLY.

IT'S DOING ITS WORK IN YOUR BLOOD. RESTRUCTURING AND MAINTAINING YOUR METABOLISM.

ADAPTING TO NEW DEMANDS.

WHAT'S SENT-CHINT?

SENTIENT.

IT MEANS CONSCIOUS. IT KNOWS US.

THIS STUFF'S ALIVE? INSIDE ME?

JONNY.

EASY.

THERE'S NOTHING TO FEAR. TRUST ME.

LISTEN...

...THE CELLS IN YOUR BODY ARE ALIVE, RIGHT?

RIGHT.

AND THAT'S NOTHING TO BE AFRAID OF, RIGHT?

RIGHT.

THIS IS NO DIFFERENT...

...EXCEPT WE CONTROL THESE CELLS. WE CAN USE THEM IN MACHINES AND IN LIVING THINGS TO...

...WELL, TO MAKE THE WORLD INTO WHAT WE WANT. DOES *THAT* SOUND WEIRD?

I DON'T KNOW.

LISTEN, JONNY. YOU'RE ONE OF US NOW.

WE'RE INVENTING THE FUTURE. WE HAVE TO GET USED TO NEW THINGS ALL THE TIME. IT'S OUR JOB. OKAY?

HEY, KID...

JONNY!

LISTEN, ABOUT YOU LIVING HERE...

...JETT GIRL SAYS SHE'S AFRAID IT'D BE A LOT OF EXTRA TROUBLE FOR HER.

WHAT?

NOW, EVERYONE AT GO BASE WORKS A VERY DEMANDING JOB...

...BUT SHE SEEMS TO THINK SHE SHOULD WORK ONLY SO HARD AND NO HARDER.

I NEVER SAID THAT--

WELL, WHAT DID YOU SAY?

TELL HIM.

YEAH, TELL ME.

PROFESSOR...

...IF I'M GOING TO BE YOUR BODYGUARD...

...DON'T MAKE ME WANT YOU DEAD.

JETT GIRL...

WHAT *IS* IT WITH YOU, PARK? WITH *EVERYONE* AROUND HERE?

WHAT?

YOU COME ON LIKE YOU EXPECT ME TO TEAR YOUR HEAD OFF.

IS IT THE *ARMOR?* WHY DOES EVERYONE TREAT ME LIKE SUCH A... SUCH A...

GROUCH?

BLESS YOU FOR NOT BEING GENDER-SPECIFIC.

FOR THE RECORD, I *LIKE* PEOPLE. I LIKE MY *JOB.* I EVEN LIKE *15-YEAR-OLDS.* EVEN *ANNOYING* ONES WHO CAN'T SIT *STILL.*

BUT...

BUT IF YOU *TREAT* ME LIKE A...

UHH--

...LIKE A GROUCH, MAYBE I'LL *RESPOND* LIKE ONE. AND BEFORE LONG MAYBE I'LL *BE* ONE. AND IT WON'T BE ALL *MY* FAULT WHEN--

THERE'S A SITUATION. IN THE SPACELAB.

WHAT?

OH GOD. LISTEN TO ME...

...FILL ME IN WHILE WE WALK.

ONE OF OUR LASER SATELLITES-- RUMSF-041560-- WENT BERSERK.

TOOK A SHOT AT THE INTERNATIONAL SPACE STATION.

WHEN?

NINE MINUTES AGO. IT'S HEADED 'ROUND FOR ANOTHER PASS.

CASUALTIES UNKNOWN. THERE'S A CREW OF 12, AND NO RESPONSE TO OUR HAILS.

THE 0415 SERIES IS SENTIENT. DID YOU TRY ZAPPING IT WITH A SLEEPER-SIGNAL?

IT'S NOT TAKING OUR CALLS.

RUMSF IS BUZZING WITH A SIGNAL THAT SOMEHOW OVERRIDES ANYTHING WE SEND. SOMEONE GOT TO ITS NANOPLASM.

NOT "SOMEONE." THE CULTIST. IT'S ALWAYS THE DAMNED CULTIST.

ALL WE CAN DO IS EUTHANIZE IT. TRIGGER ITS NANOTOXIC SACS.

EVEN IF THE SIGNAL GETS THROUGH, I'M NOT ALLOWED TO DO THAT WITHOUT AUTHORIZATION.

PROFESSOR ZERO TO THE SPACELAB!

I HOPE YOU'RE IN A BABY-KILLING MOOD...

UNCLE! WHAT IS IT?

HE'S TALKING TO THE SATELLITE. FEEDING IT TARGETS. THE STATION... NEW YORK... CHICAGO... RIGHT HERE IN DENVER.

BEETHOVEN IS PLANNING TO DIE...

...AND THEN TO KEEP KILLING.

SAY THE WORD, PROFESSOR. WE CAN STILL RELEASE THE NANOTOXIN AND AVOID ALL THIS.

HOW? WE CAN'T GET A SIGNAL THROUGH.

PREP THE **GO PLANE**. WE'LL HAVE TO DELIVER THE TOXIN IN PERSON.

I'LL GO.

TAKE JONNY WITH YOU.

WHAT?

FIRST GET HIM OUT OF THESE AWFUL STRAPS...

...THEN A SLIGHT CHARGE.

WAKE UP, JONNY.

WHOA!

SETTLE DOWN!

THERE'S A LOT OF SENSITIVE EQUIPMENT--

WHY DO YOU HAVE TO TALK TO ME LIKE I'M A LITTLE KID?

YOU'RE NOT MY BABYSITTER, SO QUIT ACTING LIKE ONE! AND QUIT RESENTING IT!

I SAID SETTLE DOWN.

DIDN'T YOU HEAR MY UNCLE? HE SENT ME UP HERE BECAUSE I'M THE HERO! I'VE BEEN WAITING FOR SOMETHING LIKE THIS...

...AND YOU'RE RUINING IT!

DO I HAVE TO STRAP YOU BACK IN?

WHAT ARE YOU DOING?

CALLING MY UNCLE.

WE DON'T HAVE TIME FOR THIS.

I'M GOING TO TELL YOU WHAT YOUR UNCLE SAID TO ME JUST BEFORE WE LEFT.

YOU WANT TO KNOW THE REAL REASON HE SENT YOU UP HERE?

...I AM YOUR BABYSITTER.

SHUT UP.

SHUT...

...UP...

SORRY TO BE ROUGH ON YOU, KID. BUT I HAVE TO FOCUS, OKAY?

KID?

OKAY?

I WANT MY PARENTS.

THE SATELLITE...

...IT FIRED AT US! BLEW US OPEN! AND YOU ALMOST GOT SUCKED OUT!

AND YOU SAVED ME?

NOT YET! WE'RE LOSING AIR--

SSSHH. IT'LL BE ALL RIGHT. WATCH.

FZAAT

JUST STAY STILL...

FSSSH

...AND DO WHAT I DO!

YOW!

KRADOOOM

AAAHH!

YOU *OK?*

NOT YET.

WE HAVE ABOUT THIRTY SECONDS TO DO WHAT WE CAME FOR...

...BEFORE THAT PSYCHO SATELLITE STRIKES AGAIN...

...SO JUST BE *QUIET* A MINUTE, OK?

AND SUDDENLY I AM DOOMED.

TO A DEATH TOO SMALL.

I WAS *SUPPOSED* TO KILL *MILLIONS.* FOR THE GLORY OF *UNREASON*—FOR THE GLORY OF MY MASTER, *THE CULTIST...*

...FOR THE GLORY OF *DR. ANGUS BEETHOVEN,* PHYSICIST OF THE *ABSURD.*

DOCTOR?

I *APOLOGIZE* FOR HOW THIS MUST *SOUND...*

...BUT KILLING *YOU* IS NOT *ENOUGH.*

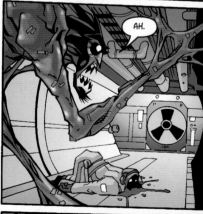

AH.

IT DOESN'T *HAVE* TO BE.

TARGET DESTROYED, PROFESSOR...

...RUMSF-041560 IS NO MORE.

WHAT A WASTE OF PARTS AND MONEY. WE COULD HAVE GOTTEN THE SAME RESULT WITH A MISSILE.

JETT GIRL WAS SUPPOSED TO GET *INSIDE* AND *POISON* IT.

DATA SUGGESTS THAT RUMSF-- OR ITS CONTROLLER-- SAW THEM COMING AND ATTACKED. SHE'D HAVE HAD NO TIME --

ATTACKED?

CALL THEM.

NOW.

I WANT TO TALK TO MY *NEPHEW.*

TRYING, SIR.

HERE'S A SIGNAL. FAINT, BUT IF I CAN LOCK IT DOWN.

GO AHEAD, PROFESSOR. THEY SHOULD HEAR YOU.

JONNY?

ARE YOU *ALL RIGHT?*

DON'T WORRY ABOUT ME.

WHEN THE TOXIN ERUPTED, JONNY'S NANOPLASMIC BLOOD REACTED. HE SAYS HE'S ALL RIGHT NOW.

NO I'M NOT. YOU *LIED* TO ME. YOU SAID YOU SENT ME ON THIS MISSION TO *HELP*.

BUT YOU JUST DID IT TO GET ME OUT OF THE *WAY*. LIKE A *BABY*.

WHAT MAKES YOU SAY THAT?

JETT GIRL TOLD ME.

JONNY!

WE'LL DISCUSS THIS IN PERSON. YOU'RE COMING HOME NOW.

HE SAYS HE'S FINE AND I BELIEVE HIM.

WE'RE NOT GOING ANYWHERE UNTIL WE SHUT BEETHOVEN DOWN.

IT'S NOT URGENT. WE TOOK HIS WEAPON.

HE'LL FIND *ANOTHER*. PROFESSOR, I THINK YOU'RE LETTING *PERSONAL* MATTERS INTERFERE WITH--

JETT GIRL...

...IF YOU LIKE WORKING HERE...

...YOU'LL BRING MY NEPHEW HOME.

NO.

FZAAK

I GUESS WE KNOW HOW TO FIND HIM.

JUST FOLLOW THE BODIES.

LET'S GET THIS OVER WITH. COME ON, KID...

...PRETEND YOU'RE NOT SCARED.

IT'LL DRIVE HIM NUTS.

WHAT ARE YOU DOING?

AAAH?

HEH.

THOUGHT I WAS ALONE.

YOU MEAN YOU THOUGHT YOU *MURDERED* EVERYONE.

JUST WHAT IS IT YOU *WANT*?

WHY, TO BE *LOVED*, OF COURSE.

AND TO ERODE OUR ORBIT. TO *BURN* ON RE-ENTRY AS THIS *PLUTONIUM* POISONS A HUGE CHUNK OF EARTH'S ATMOSPHERE.

TO PLANT *CANCERS* FROM SEA TO SHINING SEA, LIKE *APPLESEEDS.*

KZZZT

TO MEET *DEATH* AS POINTLESSLY AS *LIFE!*

UHHHH... WE'RE STILL FALLING.

DO YOU KNOW HOW TO STOP US FROM BURNING UP?

NO, BUT I'M GETTING AN IDEA. A REALLY DISGUSTING IDEA.

GRAB AN END.

WHAT?

CHECK THE DATA AGAIN!

I'VE CHECKED AND RECHECKED A HUNDRED TIMES. THE GO PLANE ISN'T THERE!

I'M SORRY, PROFESSOR! THEY'RE GONE!

WHAT HAVE I DONE.

UNCLE NOAH?

JONNY! YOU'RE ALIVE!

WE'RE BOTH FINE, SIR. WE'LL BE HOME SOON.

I'VE BEEN OUT OF MY MIND WITH WORRY! WHAT HAVE YOU BEEN DOING?

TELL HIM, KID.

COVER GALLERY
ART BY FRANCISCO RUIZ VELASCO

COVER #1

COVER #2

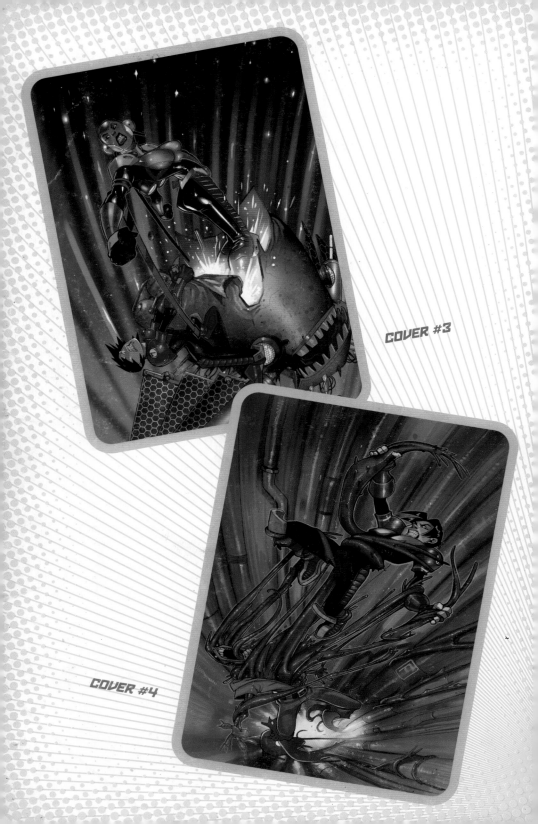

COVER #3

COVER #4